KATY GETS A JOB
a very good job

by Emma Pendergraph Slone

illustrated by Ellie Harmon

Published by Kids Book Press
An imprint of A & S Holmes Publishing, A & S Holmes, Inc.
Sharon Kizziah-Holmes – Publishing Coordinator
Springfield, Mo

ISBN -13: 978-1-956806-47-2

DEDICATION

This book is dedicated to my daughter Michele Russell, and my son Kelley Pendergraph. The best big sister and big brother two little girls could have ever had.

ACKNOWLEDGMENTS

I would like to thank two former Special Education Teachers at Springfield Public Schools. Linda Zweerink for recognizing Sara's intelligence and potential at a very early age. Carol Lieberwitz for recommending the Canine Companion Service Dog organization

I cannot leave out the many therapists who worked tirelessly with Sara and Amanda to improve their lives through physical therapy, occupational therapy and speech therapy at Springfield Public Schools.

I would also like to thank Ellie Harmon for her delightful illustrations for this book and Sharon at Paperback Press for agreeing to take on this project. Without them it would still be unfinished on my desk and on my bucket list.

Katy was a beautiful, Golden Retriever, puppy. She lived with Bryan and Susan in Michigan.

They taught Katy the skills she would need to get a job helping people.

Katy wanted to grow up and get a job; a very good job. But first, Katy had a lot to learn.

When Katy chewed up Susan's slippers, Bryan would say "STOP!" and Katy would stop.

When Katy tried to sneak bites of food from Bryan's plate, Susan would say "LEAVE IT!" and Katy would leave it alone.

Katy was not only smart and beautiful, she was very, very good, too.

When Bryan and Susan took Katy to Doggie Obedience School, she won the blue ribbon for best puppy in the class.

They were very proud of Katy.

Bryan and Susan were sure Katy would grow up someday and get a job, a very good job.

Bryan and Susan raise puppies for Canine Companions.
This is an organization that trains dogs to help people
who have a disability.

Some people cannot hear, and some cannot walk.
Some of the people who need a helper dog are children.

When Katy was 16 months old it was time to return to Canine Companions to complete her training. She missed Bryan and Susan very much and they missed her too.

At Canine Companions Katy worked very hard for Miss Vicki and Miss Cheri in her classes. She learned to turn on lights. She learned to push elevator buttons. She learned to go in under a desk and lie quietly when the people were busy.

Katy learned to pick up objects in her mouth and carry them gently.

She learned to give the object back when asked.

She even learned to pay the clerk when shopping.

FLEA
Shampoo

Surely she would get a job now. A very good job.

One day a group of people came to Canine Companions to find just the right dog to take home for a helper.

Maybe one of them will choose me, thought Katy.

I'll take this one!

When the people left two weeks later, no one had chosen Katy to be their helper.

That made Katy very sad because she wanted a forever home and a job. A very good job.

Why was Katy not chosen? Could it be because she was not pretty enough?

No, Katy was very beautiful.

Could it be because she wasn't smart enough?

1 flea + 1 flea = 23 fleas

No, Katy was very smart......for a dog.

There must be someone special Katy could love and work for... someone who wanted a dog just like her.

Sara was a young girl who wanted a trained service dog from Canine Companions.

She lived in Missouri and had waited for years and years for just the right dog.

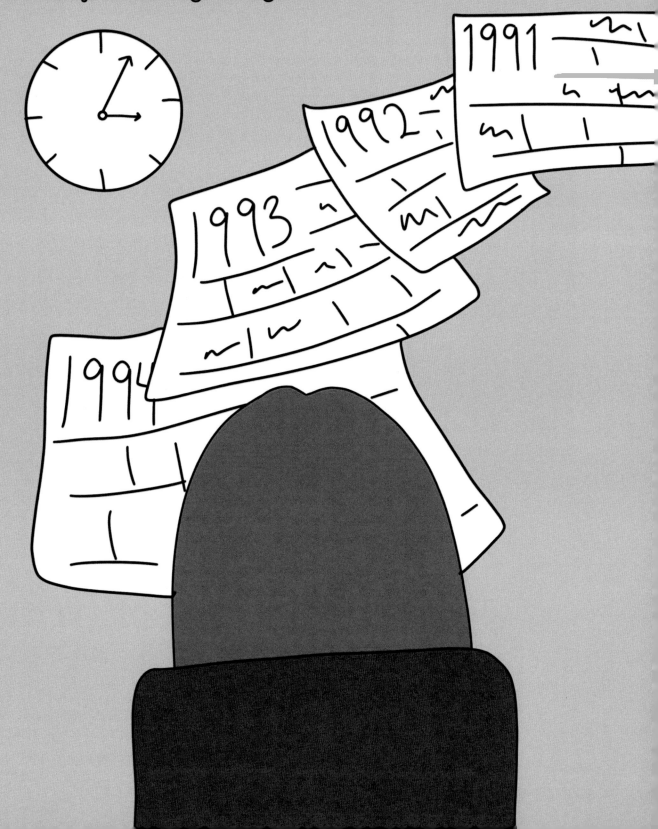

Sara could not walk so she used a wheelchair. Sara could not talk so she used a computer for speech. She really needed a special dog who could understand her computer voice.

One day Sara's phone rang. It was Miss Cheri from Canine Companions. Miss Cheri said, "Sara, I want you to come to Ohio for team training. We may have a dog that is just right for you."

Oh, that's wonderful! Thank you very much, Sara replied.

Sara was excited! She went to Ohio with her mom Emma, her dad Charlie and her sister Amanda.

Amanda was going to receive a helper dog too.

Team training was fun for Sara and Amanda.

Miss Cheri got down on the floor and pretended to be a dog. She was showing the class how dogs sometimes misbehave.

The other people in class worked very hard, too. They all wanted to pass the test that was given each day.

There were many dogs in Team Training at Canine Companions. Sara especially liked the Golden Retriever named Katy. Would Miss Cheri think Katy was right for her?

Sara watched Katy carefully. One day Sara spoke to Katy with her computer voice, "Katy, stand" and Katy stood up.

When Sara said, "Katy, sit", Katy sat down.

"Miss Cheri" cried Sara's Mom. "Come quick! Look what Katy can do. She can understand Sara's computer voice!"

"No" said Miss Cheri shaking her head. "It takes a dog a very long time to learn to respond to a computer voice; maybe 6 months or maybe even a year."

Then Sara and Katy showed Miss Cheri what they could do. Miss Cheri was impressed.

"Yes, Katy is the right dog for you," she said.

Sara was happy when she and Katy graduated from Team Training at Canine Companions.

Katy was happy, too. Now she had a forever home, someone to love and a job. A very good job!

ABOUT THE AUTHOR

Emma Pendergraph Slone was an x-ray technician by training but a childcare worker by heart. She found her true calling, working with children with disabilities after her third child Sara, was diagnosed with cerebral palsy. Emma and her husband Charles were blessed to have cared for eighty foster children over a 25 year span in addition to their four children, Michele, Kelley, Sara and Amanda.

Widowed in 2001, Emma is now married to Bob Slone. She is retired and resides in the beautiful Ozarks where she and Bob enjoy church activities, playing cards with friends and traveling. Emma also enjoys volunteering, reading, big family dinners and babysitting the great grands.

ABOUT THE ILLUSTRATOR

Ellie Harmon is a freshman in high school. She loves to draw and also enjoys listening to music and playing instruments. Ellie plays the oboe in her band at school, sings in the choir, and plays the ukulele for fun. In addition to her love of the arts, she is also an avid reader. She lives with her parents and sister in the beautiful Ozarks, along with their three dogs: Henry, Jasper, and Maggie.

ABOUT SARA

Sara was born in Missouri in 1977. She was diagnosed with cerebral palsy, the result of a traumatic brain injury at birth. She was unable to walk or speak, however, with the support of family, teachers and medical professionals she achieved amazing things. With the aid of a switch mounted under her foot she could program her voice computer to say whatever she wished. With that same switch she could maneuver her power wheelchair where she wanted to go. With a faith stronger than most adults, she invited enough wheelchair using children to church that a bus was purchased to accommodate them.

She attended a local elementary school, jr. high and graduated from high school. In the years between high school graduation and her death in October 2003, Sara and her beloved service dog Katy traveled to most of the elementary schools in two counties with their "Sara Says Storytime", a disabilities awareness program.

Katy was laid to rest in December of 2003 from bone cancer. They were inseparable best friends for nine years.

Made in the USA
Monee, IL
01 April 2022

93487516R00021